HISTORIC BRIDGES
OF PENNSYLVANIA

By

WILLIAM H. SHANK, P.E.

First Printing, First Edition, December 1966
Second Printing, Second Edition, August 1974
Third Printing, Second Edition, January 1977
Fourth Printing, Third Edition, July 1980
Fifth Printing, Third Edition, March 1986
Sixth Printing, Third Edition, September 1990
Seventh Printing, Fourth Edition, June 1997
Eighth Printing, Fourth Edition, February 2004

Published by

AMERICAN CANAL & TRANSPORTATION CENTER

FRONT COVER: A very rare photograph, made in 1869, of the original wooden-arch, Howe-truss, single track railroad bridge at Rockville, Pa., looking west. Here the main line of the Pennsylvania Railroad crossed the Susquehanna River enroute between Harrisburg and Pittsburgh. (Courtesy Benjamin F.G. Kline, Jr.)

ISBN 0-933788-33-9

This beautiful, 232-foot single-span covered bridge at Stoudt's Ferry over the Schuylkill River north of Reading was unique. It had canal-team mule towpaths on both sides to permit transfer of the towing teams from one bank to the other without disconnecting the tow line. (Courtesy of George R. Wills.)

CONTENTS

FOREWORD

The development of Pennsylvania's transportation systems during the 1800's included many interesting structures to bridge the State's numerous streams and rivers. Beginning with the turnpike and canal eras and continuing through the great railroad boom of the late 19th century, such great bridge engineers as John Roebling, Timothy Palmer, Theodore Burr, and Lewis Wernwag left their mark. In fact, many of their most notable structures were developed in the state.

Even though **Historic Bridges of Pennsylvania** focuses on a by-gone era, this 4th edition includes a chapter on bridges built in the latter part of the 20th century. As is true of most historical subjects, comparing the old with the new can be enlightening. The historic bridges detailed in this book, while primitive in design, pointed the way for the development of today's trim and reliable structures.

We are delighted that the 1997 printing has sold out, thus necessitating this 8th printing, virtually identical to its predecessor.

William H. Shank, P.E.
February 2004

Cumberland Valley Railroad Bridge at Harrisburg, using the Town lattice truss and double-deck construction. A fire destroyed the original wooden structure in 1844 and it was rebuilt two years later. In 1856 it was replaced with an iron-truss bridge. Note both sections of the "Camelback Bridge" in the background.

INTRODUCTION

On today's sophisticated super highways, we whizz along at a mile-a-minute, crossing over small streams, creeks and rivers, scarcely even realizing they are there. How different from two hundred years ago, when even a small stream, crossing our line of travel, presented problems in reaching the opposite bank. For such a stream, the crossing point selected was usually the shallowest point in the vicinity, and we "forded" the stream by simply driving our horses or wagons across at this point, hoping not to break a wheel, or a horse's ankle in pot-holes hidden beneath the water.

On larger streams, where fairly heavy traffic prevailed, we could usually count on a ferry boat, operated by a local entrepreneur, who, for a small fee would "pole" us across the river, along with our horses and wagons, on a sort of flat-bottom scow, capable of holding possibly as many as four or five wagons per trip. If the current was swift, these ferry-boats would be guided and held in their path, by "loops" (or pulleys) sliding along a long rope, or cable, extending from opposite banks of the river. Later, when steam engines were developed, these ferry-boats grew in size and were steam-driven, rather than hand-powered.

In the early 1800's, at some of the smaller stream crossings, we might even find an occasional low bridge of logs, or even loose stones, which would get us to the opposite bank without wet feet. Such primitive devices were usually washed out with each spring freshet and thus had to be replaced frequently.

The building of scientifically designed bridges, capable of withstanding normal high water and the transport of heavy loads, is an art certainly not confined to North America. The Chinese had developed cantilever bridges of sorts thousands of years before Columbus discovered America. The Romans had developed stone arch bridges, viaducts and aqueducts to a fine art, both practically and esthetically. Some of their finest works still stand today, a tribute to the skill of these artisans of two thousand years ago. South American Indians were building rope-type suspension bridges across deep chasms in the Andes long before our Pennsylvania forefathers turned their attention to bridging the streams of the State with permanent structures.

What makes the bridge-building era in Pennsylvania interesting is the fact that early bridge designers in this country, with a strong injection of the new American pioneering spirit, were willing to pin their hopes on radically new designs, untried elsewhere in the World, some of which have revolutionized the bridge building arts of the previous five thousand years.

Timothy Palmer's "Permanent Bridge" across the Schuylkill at Philadelphia—said to be America's first covered bridge.

PENNSYLVANIA BRIDGEBUILDERS OF THE EIGHTEEN HUNDREDS

Before examining the actual structures created by our pioneer bridge builders in Pennsylvania, it seems logical to investigate the builders themselves and their particular specialities in the bridge engineering field. Not all of them were native Pennsylvanians, but it was in this State that many of them found the most challenging testing ground for their ideas. In discussing their individual attributes, I have attempted to arrange them chronologically, although many of them were contemporary and their activities overlapping. Not all bridge designers of the 1800's are included; just those best remembered for their activities in Pennsylvania.

Timothy Palmer (1751-1821)

Timothy Palmer, a native of Newburyport, Massachusetts, was one of the most ingenious of the pioneer bridge builders. Completely self-taught and a self-styled "master carpenter and bridge architect," he patented his original bridge design in 1797. His reputation was made in building roofless combination arch and truss-type, long-span wooden bridges over the Merrimack, Kennebee and Connecticut Rivers in New England, not to mention his arched span across the Potomac River at Georgetown, Md.

Thus, when the directors of the Schuylkill Permanent Bridge Company of Philadelphia elected in 1801 to build a wooden structure across the Schuylkill instead of the stone arch bridge originally planned, they called on Timothy Palmer as the best-known "wood bridge" man in this country, to complete the job.

The "Permanent Bridge," located where Market Street now crosses the Schuylkill at Philadelphia, became Timothy Palmer's best-known work. During the Revolution, while the British were in possession of

Philadelphia, there was a pontoon bridge at this point and later a plank-floor bridge on floating logs. The Permanent Bridge was needed as the final link in the Lancaster-Philadelphia Turnpike. Palmer and his workmen completed the structure on two piers built earlier, between 1801 and 1805, at a cost of $300,000. The Permanent Bridge had an over-all length, including abutments and wing walls, of 1300 feet. The center span was 195 feet long with a 12 foot rise, and the two side spans were 150 feet each.

The trusswork was sufficiently completed on January 1, 1805 to permit the bridge to be opened to traffic. Palmer would have let the structure open, but Judge Richard Peters, president of the bridge company, had other ideas. He asked Palmer if the bridge would not last longer, if protected from the wind and rain by a weather-proof covering. Palmer admitted that the life span of the bridge might be increased from the normal 10 to 12 years to 30 to 40 years by doing this and a roof and sidewalls were added. Thus was created the *first covered bridge in America.* As Palmer had predicted, the bridge stood with little attention until 1850, when a fire gutted it and it was rebuilt and widened for an additional car track.

Palmer's second and last covered bridge was erected to cross the Delaware River between Easton, Pennsylvania and Philipsburg, New Jersey. Built in 1805, this two-span, covered structure weathered storm and flood for 91 years, being replaced by a steel bridge in 1896.

Looking north from the junction of the Lehigh & Delaware at Easton, Pa. Palmer's bridge crossing the Delaware at Easton was a familiar landmark for over ninety years. Note to the right the outlet lock from the Lehigh Canal system, connecting with the Morris Canal, on the New Jersey side. (Courtesy Hugh Moore, Jr.)

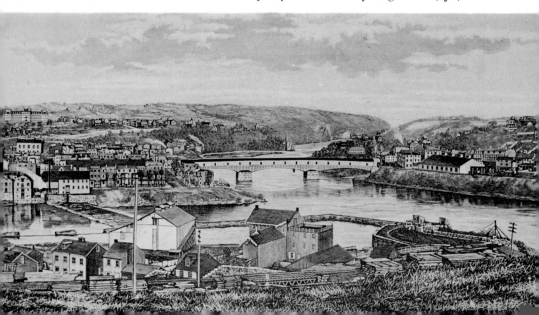

After completion of the Easton Bridge, Timothy Palmer spent his last years in semi-retirement at his Massachusetts home. He lived long enough to see the principle of the covered bridge applied to countless wooden structures in Pennsylvania and other eastern states.

James Finley (1756-1828)

One of the "unsung heroes" among early American bridge pioneers was James Finley, a native of Fayette County, Pennsylvania. Little has been recorded of the life of this western Pennsylvanian, perhaps because his patented "chain bridge" was too far ahead of its time. Indeed, except for his use of chains rather than the then unknown steel cable, his basic bridge design was virtually identical to that of the Delaware River Bridge at Philadelphia, George Washington Bridge at New York, or the Golden Gate Bridge at San Francisco.

Believed to be the son of a Reverend James Finley, who migrated to western Pennsylvania from Ireland, young "James Finley, Esquire" became, in the late 1700's, a political figure in Fayette County, serving at various times as Justice of the Peace, County Commissioner, State Representative and one of the Judges of the Court of Common Pleas of Fayette County. His term as judge began sometime before 1795, as we find a record of a case pleaded before Judge Finley on May 5, 1795.

A thoroughly successful lawyer and highly respected member of his community, Judge Finley in later life also demonstrated his ability as an inventor and engineer by developing a chain suspension bridge which was without doubt the first pier-type metal suspension bridge in the World. In the primitive rope-type suspension bridges, the floor had been laid directly on the catenary, whereas Finley's bridge had a level floor suspended from a looped span with catenary sagging one-seventh of the width of the major spans.

After experimenting with models and applying for patents, Finley built his first bridge over Jacobs Creek in 1801 on the principal turnpike between Connellsville and Mount Pleasant. A contemporary described the bridge as follows: "The bridge which Judge Finley has undertaken to erect at the expense ($600) of Fayette and Westmoreland Counties is now complete. Its construction is on principles entirely new and is perhaps the only one of its kind in the world. It is solely supported on two iron chains extending over four piers, 14 feet higher than the bridge, fastened in the ground at the ends, describing a curved line, touching the level of the bridge on the center. The bridge is of 70 foot span and 13 feet wide; the chains are of inch square bars in links from five to ten feet long; but so that there is a joist where each pendant must bear."

Sketch of one span of James Finley's patented chain bridge of 1801. The similarity between his design and the modern cable suspension bridge is strikingly apparent.

Although Finley's first bridge was built in 1801, he did not receive patent title until 1808.

Writing with great confidence of his invention in a paper published in June 1810, James Finley said, "There are eight of these bridges erected now, the largest of which is that at the Falls of the Schuylkill (Philadelphia) 306 feet span, aided by an intermediate pier, the passage eighteen feet wide, supported by two chains of inch and a half square bar . . . There are two erected near Brownsville, in Fayette County, the spans 120 and 112 feet, inch and a quarter iron, breadth 18 and 15 feet. There was one built last season over the Neshaminy in Buck's County, near 200 feet span, one pier . . . Another incorporated company at Pawling's Ford, on Schuylkill, are taking measures to erect one this summer, at that place, near 200 feet span without any pier." He also referred to bridges out of the State which he had designed.

Subsequent records indicate that Finley also designed two bridges across the Lehigh River, one 475 feet long at Northampton, Pa., in 1811, and a second at Allentown, with two spans of 230 feet each, in 1815.

A number of other Finley bridges were constructed in the next few years, in Pennsylvania and surrounding states, mainly built by others on Finley's patent rights.

Finley's first bridge at Jacobs Creek survived until 1825 when it broke under a six-horse team, but it was repaired and put in service again. His largest bridge, at Schuylkill Falls, Philadelphia, broke down when crossed by a herd of cattle in 1811. The owners sold their rights to Josiah White and Erskine Hazard, later renowned as builders of the Lehigh Canal. After a repair job and second collapse in 1816 under weight of ice and snow, White and Hazard replaced the old bridge with a small suspension bridge for pedestrian travel, only, using as the suspending medium wire from their nearby rolling mill and wire plant.

Thus to White and Hazard goes credit for having built the first wire suspension bridge in the world.

Lewis Wernwag (1769-1843)

Born in Würtemberg, Germany, Lewis Wernwag migrated to Philadelphia as a. young man of 18 years, where he started building mills, mill wheels and machinery to make whetstones and nails. His first attempt at bridge building was made in 1810-11 when he successfully built two light wooden bridges to take the Post Road from Philadelphia to New York over Neshaminy and Frankford Creeks north of Philadelphia. Both these ingenious bridges contained draw spans to permit the passage of masted vessels.

When Philadelphians organized a company to bridge the Schuylkill River at a site known as "Upper Ferry" in 1812, they selected Wernwag as the designer, because of his local reputation as a long-time master-mechanic as well as the builder of the first draw bridges in the area.

The Upper Ferry Bridge was Wernwag's masterpiece. In its day it was the longest single arch wooden bridge in America, with a clear span of 340 feet from bank to bank, unimpeded by central piers. With a rock foundation for the eastern end and 499 piles to provide a firm foundation for the western abutment, it carried the road-way 38 feet above its end

Lewis Wernwag's famous "Collossus," crossing the Schuylkill at "Upper Ferry," Philadelphia. (Courtesy Pennsylvania Historical and Museum Commission)

foundations at the mid-stream over a graceful arch, heavily supported by truss work tied to an overhead arch which also included a roof and sidewalls. It was almost immediately dubbed "The Colossus" by the local citizenry. Ornate entrances were constructed at each end and it became one of Philadelphia's "show-places."

His reputation as a bridge builder firmly established, **Lewis** Wernwag went on to build some 26 additional bridges in Pennsylvania, Maryland, Virginia, Ohio and Delaware. His Pennsylvania enterprises included bridges across the Delaware at New Hope, another Schuylkill Bridge at Reading, a bridge over the Susquehanna north branch at Wilkes Barre and, in Pittsburgh, some of that growing city's first bridges across the Allegheny and Monongahela.

During his bridge building career in Pennsylvania, he lived at Pawling's Ford where he established the Phoenix ironworks, consisting of shops and buildings, financed by Philadelphia capital (plus *another* Schuylkill River Bridge)—a settlement now known as Phoenixville, Pa. A decline in business after the War of 1812 caused the Phoenix Works to fail, and Wernwag transferred his activities to Conowingo, Maryland, and later, to Harper's Ferry, then in Virginia. A number of bridges, in and near these locations are Wernwag-designed.

Wernwag died at Harpers Ferry in 1843. His famous "Colossus" might easily have outlasted him but it was destroyed by fire in 1838, to be replaced by another record-breaking span, Ellet's suspension bridge.

Theodore Burr (1771-1822)

No relation of Aaron Burr, Theodore Burr, born in Torrington, Connecticut in 1771, became equally famous in his own right. After studying the arch-truss combinations of the contemporary wooden bridge builders, and, after considerable experimentation and the building of several models, Burr developed an arch-supported truss carrying a level roadway and patented in 1804. This became known as the "Burr Truss" and ultimately formed the basis for many of the covered bridges built in United States in the 1800's. Its distinguishing feature was a curved arch with ends firmly toed into the adjoining piers and supporting the upper and lower horizontal "chords" which formed the support for the bridge floor and roof. Multiple king posts between chords, each firmly pegged to the arch, completed the structure.

Burr's first important bridge, which some consider his masterpiece, was a four-span crossing at Troy, New York, the first over the Hudson River, with clear-spans varying from 154 to 180 feet in length. Another

The longest single-arch wooden span bridge in the world-Burr's short-lived "masterpiece," at McCall's Ferry, on the Susquehanna, near the present Holtwood Dam. (Courtesy Pennsylvania Water & Power Company)

important structure built by Burr in 1804, was a five-span bridge over the Delaware River at Trenton with spans of 161, 186, 198 and two spans 203 feet in length, which lasted for ninety years. His fame spread through upper New York State, but after building a number of bridges there, Burr decided Pennsylvania offered a more challenging field.

Further, the Pennsylvania Legislature had just authorized four new bridge companies to build spans across the Susquehanna at Northumberland, Harrisburg, Columbia and McCall's Ferry. Burr, with supreme confidence, bid on all four and obtained contracts for all but the Columbia crossing.

He began work on the first of these three major bridges at Northumberland, a twin crossing of the North Branch between Northumberland and Sunbury, in 1812. He decided to handle all three jobs on a "mass production" basis, obtaining the tremendous quantities of lumber needed from a huge saw mill which he erected at Chenango Point (now

Burr's covered bridge at Berwick crossing the Susquehanna North Branch to Nescopeck. The canal in the foreground and its short bridge were constructed about 10 years after Burr's death.

Western Section of Theodore Burr's famous "Camelback" Bridge at Harrisburg. Note Cumberland Valley Railroad Bridge under first arch. (Photo, LaRue Lemer)

Binghamton), New York, hiring raftsmen to float the lumber down the North Branch and main stem of the Susquehanna to his various sites.

Never one to do anything on a small scale, Burr also contracted for two more bridges along the way, one at Berwick (on the North Branch) and another for a toll bridge across the Susquehanna in Maryland.

Difficulties beset Burr on his Susquehanna projects almost from the outset, as he attempted to personally supervise the activities and pay the salaries of a veritable army of raftsmen, sawmill personnel, carpenters and masons scattered throughout three states.

Trading on his reputation and with a genial personality as one of his greatest assets, Theodore Burr kept his workers going, mainly on promises. Being constantly on the move, he was able to avoid most of his major creditors.

As advance payments were received from his client companies, he would distribute the money to the points where the financial pressure was greatest, until finally, and miraculously, all five bridges were completed. The last was his famous "Camelback" Bridge at Harrisburg,

Harrisburg end of the Eastern Section of the "Camelback". Note toll-house keeper's garden along river's edge. (Courtesy Harold Jones.).

10

The "Camelback" Eastern Section was destroyed by the flood of 1902. Both east and west sections of the 82-year old structure were removed at that time. (Courtesy George R. Wills)

opened to traffic in 1820. He also managed to sandwich into his busy schedule a three-span covered bridge at Bethlehem, Pa. (1816).

One of the most interesting Susquehanna structures created by Burr during this period was the bridge at McCall's Ferry, which, during its short life-span (1815-1818), boasted the longest single-span wooden arch in the world. The site of the bridge, now hidden beneath the water just above the present Holtwood Dam, was the narrowest part of the Susquehanna channel between Sunbury and the Chesapeake. At low water, it was only 348 feet wide, but with a swift current running in a channel approximately 100 feet deep.

Burr decided to span the gap with a huge 360 foot long wooden arch from the Lancaster County side to a pier on a shallow shelf on the York County side, with an additional 100-foot span from this pier to the York County shore line. Construction of the 360-foot section was done in two sections, individually erected on eight floats, lashed to the river bank until time to swing them into position. The swift current at this point, complicated by floods and storms, made the final erection of the huge span an almost impossible task with available equipment. Seizing upon an early ice jam in the river and with the assistance of hundreds of farmers from both York and Lancaster Counties, Burr finally slid his two sections into position over the ice and fastened them together, before the ice moved out again. The entire positioning process took about two weeks.

Burr was an engineering genius, with luck on his side. His good fortune on the McCall's project did not last, however, for in March of 1818 an unprecedented ice jam carried the entire structure away. The McCalls Bridge Company never rebuilt, so the stock, with which Burr had been paid, was a total loss to him.

Interior of the Western Section of the "Camelback"—left side, first span of this two-way bridge. (Courtesy Dauphin County Historical Society)

Burr's finances were by this time in extremely bad shape. His saw-mill in New York State was sold for taxes at a mere fraction of its value. He made new promises, pleading with those who owed him money, stalling his creditors and snatching at every small bridge job he could get to try to recoup his losses. He was engaged in supervising the construction of one of these small bridges over the Swatara Creek at Middletown in 1822, when he suddenly, and mysteriously, died, with scarcely enough money for a decent burial. Thus one of the greatest Pennsylvania bridge builders lies in some unknown, unmarked grave somewhere in central Pennsylvania.

Some of his greatest bridges remained as a testimonial to his genius. The final section of his famous Camelback bridge at Harrisburg was removed (not destroyed) in 1902. His bridges at Berwick, Bethlehem and Trenton remained in service throughout most of the 19th century.

His memory is today still preserved by members of The Theodore Burr Covered Bridge Society, an active organization for the preservation of covered bridges, with headquarters in Pennsylvania.

Three-span wooden covered bridge across the Lehigh River at Bethlehem, thought to have been constructed originally by Theodore Burr in 1816. Damaged by floods, it was re-built on several occasions in the 1800's and was finally replaced by the present "Hill To Hill Bridge" in 1924. (Courtesy of Jackson L. Durkee of Bethlehem Steel Corp.)

James Moore (1779-1855)

The father of James Moore, James Moore, Sr., came from England before the Revolution and settled in Perth Amboy, New Jersey. Shortly afterward, he enlisted as an American soldier in the Revolutionary War. He was captured and taken away and his family never saw him again. Young James Moore, although born in New Jersey, always considered himself a Pennsylvanian as he was "bound out" after his father's disappearance to a German cabinet-maker at Northumberland at an early age. His formal education, such as it was, was given him by his "master" and he learned to read and write in German rather than English!

After his apprenticeship was complete, James Moore is said to have settled at Snydertown, east of Sunbury, and in his late twenties, shifted his attention from cabinet-making to bridge building. Moore became a devoted follower of the spectacular Theodore Burr, and even before Burr came to Northumberland in 1812, Moore had built his first small bridge over Buffalo Creek at Lewisburg.

Unlike Burr, however, Moore carried each bridge job to completion before starting the next.

From small bridges in his own area, he graduated to larger projects such as the Clarion River Bridge at Clarion, Pa., built in 1821 and a 1000-foot long bridge over Little Conestoga Creek near Lancaster, Pa.

The first Columbia-Wrightsville Bridge, built by Jonathan Walcott in 1812—world's longest covered wooden bridge. (Courtesy Historical Society of York County)

The second Columbia-Wrightsville Bridge, built by James Moore, was burned by Union militia June 28, 1863, to keep Confederate troops from invading Lancaster County. This dramatic contemporary sketch by A. Berghaus was published in Frank Leslie's "Illustrated Newspaper" (New York), looking west from the Columbia side.

We now turn to the Susquehanna River Bridge at Columbia, built by Jonathan Walcott of Connecticut, in 1812.

This bridge, 5690 feet long, carried on 28 piers of 200 feet span each, was the longest covered wooden bridge in the world, unsuccessfully bid upon by Theodore Burr, but constructed by Walcott in collaboration with two local mason-carpenters, Henry and Samuel Slaymaker. This monster bridge was Walcott's outstanding effort and his only one in Pennsylvania.

The third Columbia-Wrightsville covered bridge was built by Pennsylvania Railroad in two sections (1869) with a two-span open metal truss "fire break" in the center. Ironically this bridge was destroyed, not by fire, but by a windstorm, which blew down all the wooden spans in 1896, to leave only the center "fire break" standing.

The fourth Columbia-Wrightsville prefabricated steel truss bridge was erected in 21 days. Construction is shown in progress here. Like its predecessors, it carried both railroad and vehicular traffic, and also pedestrians. It was dismantled in 1964.
(Courtesy Benjamin F. G. Kline, Jr.)

In 1832, an ice jam and flood carried Walcott's masterpiece away and James Moore went to Columbia to bid on the rebuilding. He was low bidder out of eleven competitors, and got the job for $123,247. Thus Moore had the distinction of re-building, in a slightly different location, the world's longest covered bridge, now reduced to 5620 feet in length.

It is said that James Moore was involved in the design of the Northern Central Railroad bridge at Dauphin, Pennsylvania, whose piers may still be seen in the Susquehanna River at that point.

James Moore, and his son, James Moore III, were quite active in the founding of Bucknell University at Lewisburg in 1846. James Moore, II died March 29, 1855, a highly respected member of his community.

Setting the wooden forms for the reinforced concrete arches of the fifth Columbia-Wrightsville Bridge in 1929. In the background may be seen the double-deck, steel bridge of 1897. (Courtesy of Robert S. Mayo, P.E., of Lancaster, who assisted with the construction.)

The fifth Columbia-Wrightsville Bridge was completed in 1930. It is a fine example of graceful reinforced concrete arch construction popular in the early 1900's and is said to be the longest multiple-arch highway bridge in the world. This bridge was declared a National Historic Civil Engineering landmark in 1984. (Photo by the author.)

The sixth Columbia-Wrightsville Bridge opened to traffic in November of 1972. Preliminary design work on the relocation of U.S. Route 30 and this Susquehanna River crossing was done by Buchart Horn. Final design was handled by Brookhart and Tyo, with construction by G.A. & F.C. Wagman. (Photo by the author.)

Ithiel Town (1784-1844)

Worthy of note, in Pennsylvania bridge history, is Ithiel Town, a New Haven, Connecticut architect, born in 1784. Town, observing the rigidity of lattice-pattern decorative structures, such as rose-arbor climbing frames, took the basic idea, developed it and patented it as the Town (Lattice) Truss in 1820. It was exceedingly simple, consisting of two series of parallel members running at approximately 45 degrees with the horizontal, and at right angles to each other, firmly bound together at the intersection joints. It was a good truss, easy to build, and caught on rapidly.

Town brought his truss to Pennsylvania in the early 1830's. More businessman than builder, he teamed up in Philadelphia with a master carpenter, Amos Campbell, who erected Town bridges over the Schuylkill at the Fall's in Philadelphia, over the Delaware at Centre Bridge and Yardleyville, and over the Conestoga at Lancaster. Town's design was also used extensively by Moncure Robinson in 1834 on some of the first bridges of the Philadelphia and Reading railroad.

Two outstanding lattice bridges in Pennsylvania were personally promoted by Ithiel Town.

The first was the Cumberland Valley Railroad Bridge across the Susquehanna at Harrisburg, built in 1835-36 by William M. Roberts of Philadelphia—the first combined railroad and highway bridge in America. A single track rail line was laid on the roof and a two-lane roadway inside. The bridge had twenty-two piers and was 4277 feet long.

The second was the Gray's Ferry bridge, where the Philadelphia, Wilmington and Baltimore Railroad entered Philadelphia from the south, built in 1837-38 on the Town design. It was an 800 foot long, five-span, bridge—also a combination railroad and highway structure, and the pride of the railroad when completed.

Ithiel Town, for the most part, made his money through collection of royalties on his patents, which covered both wood and metal lattice-type bridges. Very few Town type metal bridges were built in this country. One of the few was the Pittsburgh and Lake Erie Railroad Bridge over the Allegheny River at Pittsburgh.

William Howe (1803-1852)

William Howe, of Spencer, Massachusetts, was born in 1803. Howe, a millwright, observed the local use of a truss developed by Col. Stephen H. Long, a contemporary of Ithiel Town, and set out to build a better one. The truss he developed was essentially a wood cross inscribed in a rectangle, with the vertical sides of the rectangle formed by adjustable iron rods (in tension) instead of wood timbers, as in the Long truss. So similar was Howe's design to Long's that the latter claimed patent infringements for years.

Despite this, Howe's truss was patented in 1840, as an "improved design." The improvement stemmed from the adjustability of the vertical iron rods as the wood in the cross members shrank or seasoned. Thus, green, fresh-cut timbers could be used and the proper tension subsequently maintained by bolts or turnbuckles on the rods.

The Howe truss became the most popular truss in bridge construction during the latter half of the nineteenth century, and also represented the transition from wood to metal bridge construction.

Artist's sketch of the first Pennsylvania Railroad Bridge in 1848 at Rockville, Pa., using Howe truss. For an actual photograph of this bridge, see the cover illustration on this book. Note the Pennsylvania Canal in the foreground, on the east bank of the Susquehanna. Note Northern Central R.R. Bridge upstream.

Like Ithiel Town, Howe was more promoter than builder. Howe's brother-in-law, Daniel Stone, was given the exclusive franchise for Howe construction in Pennsylvania, and in 1848, Stone began work on the tremendous Rockville bridge north of Harrisburg, where the new Pennsylvania Railroad crossed the Susquehanna. Stone used 23 spans in his construction, for a total length of 3670 feet. In addition to the Howe trusses, *below* the roadbed, he added, for additional strength, Burr-type arches on the outsides of each span. This bridge withstood Susquehanna floods for twenty-eight years.

Photo of the original single-track Rockville Bridge, looking West, circa 1869.

The Rockville bridge "sold" the Howe truss in Pennsylvania, and Stone was besieged with the new royalty applications. So busy was he with the resulting paper work that he scarcely had time to take any bridge building contracts himself.

Present Pennsylvania Railroad Bridge at Rockville, built in 1902—the longest stone arch railroad bridge in the world, with forty-eight 70-foot spans for a total length of 3830 feet. Declared a National Historic Civil Engineering Landmark in 1979. (Photo by the author.)

The Howe truss principle was applied to new and existing wooden railroad bridges. This railroad bridge, thought to be the interior of the Northern Central Railroad Bridge at Dauphin, shows the application of the vertical Howe-type iron rods, in addition to basic Burr arches.

He did, however, find time to build another big Howe truss bridge in 1850 to take the place of Palmer's old Permanent Bridge at the Market Street crossing of the Schuylkill in Philadelphia. The Palmer bridge was acquired by the Philadelphia and Columbia Railroad, and Stone replaced

Ellet's 1842 wire-suspension bridge at Philadelphia, across the Schuylkill. The double outlet locks of the Schuylkill Navigation System appear in the foreground. (Courtesy of Dr. Emory L. Kemp, West Virginia University.)

it with a stronger, level-floor bridge which permitted the state-owned railroad to bring its lines directly into the heart of Philadelphia from the west, avoiding the cumbersome Belmont inclined plane.

Charles Ellet (1810-1862)

Exactly when the trend to metal bridges began in America is difficult to "pin-point." We have already pointed out that at least one exponent of metal bridges, James Finley, was at work about fifty years ahead of his time. The first *cast-iron bridge in America* was built in 1839 at Dunlap's Creek in Brownville, Pa., as part of the old National Road. This replaced one of James Finley's first chain suspension bridges, which collapsed under the combined weight of a particularly heavily loaded road wagon, plus a heavy snowfall.

A native Pennsylvanian, Col. Charles Ellet became the first of the great metal suspension bridge builders, using wire cable instead of chains. Born at Penn Manor, near Bristol, Pa., in 1810, Charles Ellet early evidenced unusual mathematical ability. As a young man he learned surveying and engineering on the canals and earned enough money to complete his engineering education abroad.

At twenty-two, with a boldness and originality of thought which marked his entire career, he presented to Congress a proposal to build a 1000-foot suspension bridge over the Potomac at Washington! His design was so far ahead of its time that he received little encouragement from Congress. Undiscouraged, he continued to write articles promoting the use of the suspension type bridge. In 1841-42, he was commissioned to build his first wire suspension bridge across the Schuylkill at Philadelphia, to replace Wernwag's timber "Colossus." It had a span of 358 feet and was supported by wire cables, five to a side. This bridge was the first major bridge of its kind in America and was considered an engineering feat of the first magnitude. It remained in use until 1874.

His reputation made, Ellet proceeded to build additional, and larger, cable suspension bridges at Wheeling on the Ohio in 1846-49, as well as the first railroad suspension bridge in 1848 over the Niagara River, and a basket ferry, the same year, over the Niagara Gorge.

Various other engineering projects occupied Ellet's attention until the outbreak of the Civil War. He perfected a plan for destroying warships by means of steam battering rams and was in command of a fleet of nine such rams during the Battle of Memphis, June 6, 1862.

Although the outcome of the battle was a Union victory, Col. Charles Ellet received a mortal wound and died several weeks later.

John Roebling, one of the pioneers in the successful construction of a number of cable-type suspension bridges in America, for canals and highways.

Charles Ellet, who built the first wire suspension bridge across the Schuylkill. He had been a staunch advocate of suspension bridges for years.

John Augustus Roebling (1806-1869)

The life of John Roebling reads like a Horatio Alger novel. Born in the town of Muhlhausen in Thuringen, Prussia , Roebling grew to young manhood in an atmosphere of military intrigue during and following the Napoleonic Wars.

John Roebling's father was a drab German merchant who ran a pipe shop. It was Roebling's mother who recognized her son's unusual talents and saw that he got the best education available, in the Royal Polytechnic School of Berlin, majoring in architecture and engineering.

After graduation, with the degree of civil engineer (1826), young Roebling built roads and bridges for the Prussian Government. The work was dull and routine and Roebling became restless. A friend, just returned from America, painted glowing pictures of the opportunities there, and John Roebling and his brother, Karl, quietly organized a small group in Muhlhausen to move to the New World and start a colony.

The 1830 Revolution in France caused severe restrictions of freedom in Germany. It became illegal for a German technician to leave the country. This merely strengthened Roebling's determination to go to America. He continued plotting to take his followers out of the country, and was listed by the police as one of the most dangerous liberals in Muhlhausen.

In a real cloak-and-dagger type operation and aided by his mother, Roebling and his followers secretly and individually made their way to Bremen, where they chartered a boat and made their escape. After eleven weeks at sea, during which time they were blown off their course by heavy winds and chased by pirates, they landed at Philadelphia, in the summer of 1831.

Under the leadership of John Roebling, the group purchased seven thousand acres of land in Butler County, Pennsylvania (north of Pittsburgh) and set up a thriving little farm community, which they named Germania. The name was later changed to Saxonburg.

Farm life was not for Roebling, and after obtaining his U.S. citizenship he applied for work on the Pennsylvania State Canal System and became assistant engineer on the Beaver and Erie Division Canal.

Later, he was assigned to run surveys for a permanent rail line over Allegheny Mountain between Johnstown and Hollidaysburg.

Canal traffic between these two water termini was already being handled by the famous Allegheny Portage Railroad, which consisted of a series of ten inclined planes, motivated by stationary steam engines, which raised or lowered the canal passengers, freight (and even whole canal boats) over Allegheny Mountain.

A typical inclined plane on the Allegheny Portage Railroad. Here John Roebling conceived the idea for steel cables to replace the dangerous hemp ropes first used on these planes.

Roebling's first highway suspension bridge over the Monongahela at Smithfield Street, 1847. This was replaced by Lindenthal's famous "bow-string" truss bridge in 1881. (Courtesy Dr. George Swetnam.)

Observing the operation of the steep planes, which carried the cars and boats upward or downward at the end of large hemp ropes, Roebling was shocked to witness the breaking of one of the ropes, causing a wreck in which two men were killed. Apparently this was a common occurrence on the "Portage."

The accident set Roebling to thinking about an article he had read in a German paper concerning the manufacture of wire rope at Freiburg, Saxony. He could not remember the details but it set him to investigating how a flexible wire rope could be made, which would not wear out as fast as the hemp, and would have far greater strength with considerably less cross-sectional area. No such thing had ever been heard of in America.

Returning to his farm in Saxonburg, he bought a quantity of iron wire and after experimentation, and with the help of his neighbors, succeeded in twisting a series of individual wires into America's first twisted wire cable. The desirable qualities of this cable were surprising even to Roebling himself. Within short order Roebling's cables supplanted the old hemp ropes on the Portage Railroad.

The latent possibilities of wire cable in other applications were at first not apparent. It took the imagination of John Roebling himself to visualize wire cables applied to bridge-building. He recalled as a youth in Germany having seen a suspension bridge of chain construction, perhaps similar to Janes Finley's almost-forgotten chain bridge of the early 1800's. Roebling visualized his new wire cable applied to large suspension bridges. He followed Charles Ellet's activities with great interest.

Roebling had an opportunity in 1844 to put his own bridge theories into practice. That year the old wooden aqueduct which brought the Pennsylvania Canal into downtown Pittsburgh was rated as unsafe by the Canal engineers.

Built in 1829, the old aqueduct consisted of seven wooden arch spans of 150 feet open span each. The tremendous weight of water was too much for this structure and breakdowns of individual arches had been a problem ever since its construction. A fire in 1845 hastened the necessity for a solution.

Roebling felt the problem could be solved with a "Bundled" wire cable suspension structure and laid his plans before the canal engineers, admitting quite frankly that it was a new type cable never applied to bridge building in America. There was considerable opposition but Roebling was finally told to proceed. He rebuilt the seven-span structure with 162-foot slack spans of two 7-inch diameter bundles of 1900 wires each, laid parallel to each other, taking great care to insure equal tension in each wire. Each cable was protected and tightly bound together by an external wrapping of annealed wire. The slack spans of these cables supported the water flume.

The success of Roebling's first structure in Pittsburgh led immediately to another—a suspension replacement to the Smithfield Street Bridge over the Monongahela in 1847, on the piers of the old wooden structure destroyed by the Great Fire of 1845. This unusual structure had eight suspension spans of 188 feet each, supported by two 4-1/2 inch diameter cables. It had cast iron suspension towers 16 feet high and

Canal boat crossing Roebling's two-span aqueduct across the Lackawaxen River on the Delaware and Hudson Canal. (Collection of Jim Shaughnessy)

25

a 35 foot roadway which carried two lines of car tracks, pedestrian promenades on both sides, and the heaviest kind of street traffic, for the next 35 years.

Roebling's reputation as a bridge builder spread rapidly and he was petitioned by a number of canal companies both in and out of Pennsylvania to assist them with their canal aqueduct problems.

Another of his aqueduct projects in Pennsylvania was the double-crossing of the Delaware and Hudson Canal over both the Lackawaxen and Delaware Rivers near their junction. Formerly a dam-created, slack-water crossing of the Delaware River only, the D. & H. had problems with the river raftsmen, who sued continually for damages incurred while crossing the D. & H. dam, and who were in constant conflict with the rope ferry crossing of D. & H. canal boats, at right angles to their line of travel.

The managers of the canal in 1846 elected to build two aqueducts at this point to correct their difficulties and called in John Roebling as one of two bidders on the job.

Roebling's competition proposed a five-pier covered bridge crossing the Delaware, contrasted to Roebling's three-pier cable-supported spans. After inspection of Roebling's aqueduct at Pittsburgh, the management awarded him the contract.

Roebling soon began work on this double-aqueduct crossing at a combined cost of $60,400. The two aqueducts were completed and opened in the Spring of 1849. The Lackawaxen aqueduct was a fairly easy two-span suspension crossing, whereas the Delaware aqueduct had four spans for a total length of 600 feet. The cable supports on the sides of the aqueduct contained 2150 wire strands each and were 8-1/2 inches in diameter. Width of the canal channel was 19 feet.

So well was this aqueduct constructed that after the abandonment of the D. & H. canal (in 1899) the aqueduct was converted into a highway crossing and is still in use today—132 years since its erection.

Another of Roebling's Pennsylvania suspension structures, built in 1859, replaced the 1819 wooden Sixth Street Bridge across the Allegheny River at Pittsburgh. This bridge was Roebling's fanciest, with ten 45-foot high cast-iron supporting towers, two 344-foot center spans and two 171-foot side spans for a total length of 1030 feet. The deck, 40 feet wide, including two 10-foot pedestrian promenades, was supported by four cables, two 7-inches and two 4-inches in diameter. (See photo.)

Roebling's four-span, 600-foot aqueduct on the Delaware and Hudson Canal, crossing the Delaware River, near Lackawaxen, Pa., completed in 1849. After abandonment as a canal crossing it was converted to a highway bridge and is still in use today. Designated a National Historic Engineering Landmark in 1972. (Collection of Jim Shaughnessy)

John Augustus Roebling, engineering genius and adopted son of Pennsylvania, died July 22, 1869, of an injury received while running surveys for the Brooklyn Bridge. It remained for his son, Colonel Washington Roebling to complete, in 1883, John Roebling's greatest triumph in America, which has set the pattern for tremendous river crossings throughout the world—the famous, still-operating Brooklyn Bridge.

Roebling's ornate bridge over the Allegheny at Sixth Street in Pittsburgh was described at the time of its opening in 1860 as the "finest and most beautiful bridge in the world." (Courtesy Benjamin F.G. Kline, Jr.)

Adolphus Bonzano (1830-1913)

Adolphus Bonzano was born in Ehingen, Wurtemburg, Germany, December 5, 1830. His father, Nicholas Anton Bonzano, was one of the Texas colonizers. After early schooling in Germany, young Adolphus came to Philadelphia (1850) to study English. Shortly afterward, he apprenticed himself to the Reynolds Machine Works in Springfield, Massachusetts, where he supplemented his academic studies with practical shop experience and soon became a skilled mechanical superintendent. He was subsequently employed by various railroad firms, which led him into bridge construction work.

In 1865 he became superintendent of bridge construction with the Detroit Bridge and Iron Works. In 1868 Bonzano joined Clark Reeves and Company, later the Phoenix Bridge Company, at Phoenixville, Pa., where he became a partner, chief engineer and vice president. He spent the next 25 years with this firm, during which time he was directly involved in the erection of a number of notable bridges.

While Rudolph Hering of Philadelphia is credited with the design of the Girard Avenue Bridge in that city (1873-74), Bonzano handled the details of construction. At the time of its completion, it was said to have been the largest high bridge in America. (100-feet in width). Tyrell rates it as "one of the finest examples of American City Bridges". It adjoined the Zoological Gardens and was built in preparation for the Philadelphia Centennial at a cost of $267,000.

Girard Avenue Bridge in Philadelphia--1873. Rated as the widest high bridge in America at the time. (Courtesy American Society of Civil Engineers.)

28

Kinzua Viaduct, built in 1882 by Bonzano in 94 days. The original structure was wrought-iron; the replacement structure of 1900 (shown in the insert) was steel. (From Mabel Caverly, courtesy of Walter Casler. Insert, courtesy of J. Hayward Madden.) See also the back-cover illustration.

Bonzano also took a major part in the reconstruction of the Columbia Bridge in Fairmount Park, Philadelphia, circa 1886, replacing the old wooden bridge which had been part of the "Main-Line" Canal-Railroad System of the early 1800's. He also directed the reconstruction of the Susquehanna Bridge at Sunbury about 1881.

However Bonzano's outstanding bridge construction project was the Kinzua Viaduct on the New York, Lakeshore and Western Railroad and Coal Company in northwestern Pennsylvania which spanned the 2052-foot wide valley of Kinzua Creek, using twenty warren type truss towers, 301 feet above water level.

Bonzano had been approached by General Thomas L. Kane, owner of the N.Y.L.W. & C. when the bridge was contemplated and asked if it were possible to build such a structure--higher than any viaduct yet known. Bonzano is said to have replied: "We'll build you a bridge a thousand feet high, if you'll provide the money!" The General had the money, and Bonzano joined with Oliver W. Barnes, chief engineer of the railroad, in planning the first Kinzua Viaduct.

Construction began May 10th, 1882 and just 94 working days later a crew of forty men had completed the highest railroad viaduct in the world. This amazing feat involved the erection of 3,105,000 pounds of wrought iron work, which later proved inadequate for the increasingly heavy railroad rolling stock and was replaced (in 1900) with a heavier (6,715,000-pound) steel structure. The railroad discontinued use of the bridge around 1956. Later acquired by the state park system, it collapsed from a tornado on July 21, 2003.

Lindenthal's unusual "Double Bow-String" Bridge over the Monongahela at Smithfield Street in Pittsburgh. Still in use, after ninety-nine years. Designated a National Historic Civil Engineering Landmark in 1975. (Courtesy Carnegie Library of Pittsburgh.)

Gustav Lindenthal (1850-1935)

Sometimes called the "dean of American bridge engineers", Gustav Lindenthal was born in Brunn, Moravia (Austria) May 21,1850. He studied at Provincial College in Brunn and Vienna, worked for a short time in the engineering department of Austrian Empress Elizabeth, and became a division engineer with the Swiss National Railroad, before emigrating to the United States in 1874. He started work in this country as a journeyman stone mason but soon after became assistant engineer of construction of the buildings for the Philadelphia Centennial, 1874-1877.

Lindenthal moved to Pittsburgh in 1877, where he was an engineer with Andrew Carnegie's bridge-building firm -- the Keystone Bridge Company. After a few years with Keystone, he was offered a position as Bridge Engineer for the Atlantic and Great Western Railroad, with whom he worked for several more years, before establishing himself in engineering private practice in Pittsburgh in 1881. Subsequently he handled numerous major bridge design projects in and near Pittsburgh.

His most notable Pittsburgh structure, designed in 1881, was the third (and present) Smithfield Street Bridge over the Monongahela River, replacing John Roebling's suspension bridge of 1847. Lindenthal widened his structure by the addition of extra trusses, for a trolley section, about 1889. This unusual bridge with its 360-foot, double-bowstring, lenticular trusses-- is now a historic landmark.

McKees Rocks Bridge across the Ohio below Pittsburgh, almost a "dead-ringer" for Lindenthal's Hell Gate Bridge. In the background is the famous Jacks Run bridge of 1931. (Courtesy of Myron Sharp.)

Another of Lindenthal's major projects in Pittsburgh was the Seventh Street Suspension Bridge over the Allegheny River, erected in 1884. It had three towers with two river spans of 330 feet and two shore spans of 165 feet, with a 90-foot truss over adjacent railroad tracks. This bridge was replaced 1925-1926 by the present suspension bridge.

While working out of Pittsburgh, Lindenthal also designed continuous truss bridges at Herr'sIsland and McKeesport and replaced numerous of the old wooden Howe-truss bridges with iron structures, to handle the much heavier locomotives then being introduced.

He moved to New York City in 1902 to become Commissioner of Bridges there and subsequently designed many more outstanding bridges until the time of his death in 1935. During this period he is best remembered for his famous Hell Gate Bridge over the East River at New York -- often referred to as "one of the greatest arch bridges of all time".

Ralph Modjeski (1861-1940)

If Ralph Modjeski had chosen a career in music instead of engineering, the World might have gained a famous concert-pianist but would have lost one of its finest bridge designers.

Born "Rudolphe Modrzejewski" in Cracow, Poland January 27,1861, Modjeski early in his American career changed his name to "Ralph Modjeski." He found that Americans had great difficulty pronouncing, spelling or remembering his complex Polish name. His mother, a famous Polish Shakespearian actress, who brought her family to the United States in 1876, had the same problem, and upon the earnest advice of her American billing agent changed her name from Mme. Helena Opid Modrzejewska to simply "Madame Modjeska".

Ralph Modjeski's European education, in addition to languages and mathematics, included musical studies under Casimir Hofmann, son of the renowned Josef Hofmann. During this period he was a fellow student with his later illustrious compatriot, Jan Ignace Paderewski. He was an extremely proficient pianist; in seven lessons he had learned four of Kohler's etudes by heart and almost the entire sixth sonata of Mozart. Chopin's nocturnes were his favorites for relaxation. Till the time of his death, he frequently spent several hours a day at the piano.

Graceful lines and staunch utility have always characterized the work of Ralph Modjeski and his firm. Illustrated here is his 330-foot, masonry-faced arch carrying Henry Avenue in Philadelphia across Wissahickon Creek. Completed in 1932. (Courtesy of Modjeski and Masters.)

However, engineering finally won out, and Ralph Modjeski elected to complete his education at the Ecole des Ponts et Chaussees in Paris, where he graduated in 1885, leading his class, with the degree of Civil Engineer.

With his family already in America, Modjeski returned to the United States, becoming a naturalized citizen in 1887. He began his engineering career in Chicago, where he worked for several years in association with George S. Morison, one of the leading bridge builders of the day.

In 1893 he decided to embark on private practice in the bridge design field and opened an office in Chicago in partnership with an engineer named Nickerson. Although this partnership lasted only a year, Modjeski went on alone to obtain his first major project -- the design and construction of a seven-span combined railway and highway bridge over the Mississippi at Rock Island, Illinois which he handled with speed and efficiency. Later he developed a set of standard bridge designs for the Northern Pacific Railroad, which remained effective for many years. From this point he rapidly progressed, alone or in partnership with others, to the design of an almost unbelievable number of the country's finest major bridges.

Frank M. Masters of Harrisburg, was employed by Modjeski in 1904 and the partnership of Modjeski and Masters was formed in 1924. Today this firm continues to operate from offices in Harrisburg, New Orleans, Chicago, Washington, D.C. and Poughkeepsie, N.Y., in the same tradition established by Ralph Modjeski.

Space does not permit listing the many major bridge projects in which Modjeski and his various partners were involved. It is significant that Modjeski was called upon to head up a new team of consultants (after several disastrous failures) in the construction of the world's longest cantilever-truss rail bridge at Quebec, Canada. Modjeski's team brought the project to a successful conclusion in 1918. He was also chairman of a board of consulting engineers in charge of the design and construction of the great eight mile-long Transbay Bridge at San Francisco, 1931-37. In Pennsylvania, he designed what, at the time, was the longest suspension bridge in the world -- the present Ben Franklin Bridge at Philadelphia (1926) and a few years later the unusual, tied-arch Tacony-Palmyra Bridge further upstream on the Delaware (1929). Some of the most interesting Pennsylvania bridges which Modjeski and his partners have produced are illustrated in this booklet. All of them are still in use, many of them winning national awards for their artistry of design.

Excitement reigned in Philadelphia in 1926 when President Calvin Coolidge, assisted by the Army Air Force, opened Ralph Modjeski's "Longest suspension bridge in the world" across the Delaware River. (Courtesy of Modjeski and Masters.)

33

EARLY TURNPIKE BRIDGES

The Pennsylvania Road

The opening of the 19th Century in Pennsylvania found the state with only a few roads binding the State together. One of these was the Pennsylvania Road which today, with slightly altered route in South Central Pennsylvania, is our well-known Lincoln Highway, or U.S. Route 30, connecting Philadelphia and Pittsburgh. This road was formed by slow development of the old Allegheny and Raystown paths followed by the Indians. First, Governor Morris of Pennsylvania, ordered the chopping of trees to widen the path from Carlisle to Bedford in 1755. The western section, from Raystown to Fort Pitt, was dubbed "Forbes Road,"

A typical secondary wooden road bridge of the 1800's. Because of the low side walls, the bridge structure is clearly visible. This bridge, still standing, is a Burr type, 80-feet long, crossing the Raystown branch of the Juniata in Bedford County, Pa. (Photo by Gertrude E. Harley)

A most unusual short span "covered bridge" at Ralph Stover State Park near Point Pleasant in Bucks County, Pa. Note the two side structures, only, are covered to protect them from the weather. (Photo by Gertrude E. Harley)

34

Another typical small crossing covered bridge known as Luther Mills Bridge in Burlington Township, Bradford County, Pa. (Photo by Elmira Star Gazette)

as it was opened in 1758 at the direction of General John Forbes as a transportation and supply route for his victorious campaign against Fort Duquesne. After the Revolution, the eastern section of the route was paved with stone (1795) to become the first long-distance paved road in the country. This section was known as the Philadelphia and Lancaster Turnpike. Finally, in 1820, paving of the entire route from Lancaster through Harrisburg to Pittsburgh was completed—an engineering triumph for the State. Two important bridges on the route were Timothy Palmer's "Permanent Bridge" at Philadelphia, and Theodore Burr's "Camelback Bridge" at Harrisburg. A three-arched stone bridge across Brandywine Creek, costing $12,000, was part of the project.

There were several other important early highways running through Pennsylvania. One was the Coastal Route, now known as U.S. Route 1, starting in New England and connecting New York, Philadelphia, Baltimore, and points south.

In 1726, James Trent was granted the right to operate a ferry at Trent's Town to provide a crossing of the Delaware River north of Philadelphia on the important Philadelphia-New York road. Following the Revolution, traffic increased so rapidly on this road that New Jersey officially recognized in 1798 the need for "a good and permanent bridge" across the Delaware at Trent's Town, a recommendation seconded by the Pennsylvania Assembly. Thus was built Theodore Burr's famous inter-state bridge at Trenton, a covered wooden arch, truss span, erected

The original Brownsville (Pa.) covered bridge, which carried the National Pike over the Monongahela River, circa 1890. (Courtesy Dr. George Swetnam)

35

Also at Brownsville, where the National Road crossed Dunlap's Creek, still standing today, this bridge, the first iron bridge in the United States, was built in 1839. Designated a National Historic Civil Engineering Landmark in 1978. (Courtesy Dr. George Swetnam)

at a cost of $180,000 between May 1804 and January 1806 by the Delaware River Bridge Company, headed by General John Beatty as president. The route from Philadelphia to New York was not completely "turnpiked" (covered with stone) until about 1812. The road became of strategic importance when, during the War of 1812, the British blockaded coastal shipping lanes. The Trenton Bridge was a key link in this important route, which ultimately extended from Portland, Maine, to Savannah, Georgia.

The National Road

Another important highway of the early 1800's, passing through Pennsylvania, was the National Road (or Cumberland Road), the first important road in the country to be built with Federal funds. Now known as U.S. Route 40, its location was selected by a board of Commissioners under Thomas Jefferson and it originally connected Baltimore with Wheeling (then in Virginia) on the Ohio River, via Cumberland, Maryland; Brownsville, Pennsylvania and Washington, Pennsylvania. It was officially opened in 1818 and shared east-west traffic with the Pennsylvania Road, ultimately being extended as far as Illinois, in 1830.

A Stage-Coach of the early 1800's, the type which traveled the turnpikes and highways of Pennsylvania.

Built in 1799 with $20,000 raised by lottery, the Perkiomen Bridge at Collegeville, Pa., is one of the oldest bridges in the State still in use. (Photo by the author.)

Several interesting bridges were located along the National Road in Pennsylvania. One was the *first iron bridge in the United States*, located at Brownsville, Pa., where the National Road crossed Dunlap's Creek. There had been several bridges at this point previously—one a chain suspension bridge by James Finley, which collapsed in 1820 under a heavy weight of snow.

Captain Richard Delafield of the U.S. Army Corps of Engineers, who had been placed in charge of reconstruction of the National Road in 1832, conceived the idea of an iron bridge at this point because of the proximity of the Brownsville foundries. The bridge had a span of 80 feet with an 8-foot rise and five arched ribs spaced at 5.77-foot intervals. Completed in 1839, the bridge is still in use today—handling high speed traffic and loads never dreamed of by the designer.

Another unusual bridge on the National Road, whose remains are today preserved by the State, was the famed "S-Bridge" five miles southwest of Washington, Pa. A two-span stone arch bridge, its main stem ran

Stone arch bridge at Lewistown, Pa., built in 1813, as part of a secondary turnpike from Harrisburg to Pittsburgh, still standing as an historic monument. (Photo by the author.)

The Somerfield Bridge, where the National Road crossed the Youghiogheny River, now under water. (Photo by the Pennsylvania Historical and Museum Commission)

at right angles to the stream, for economy of materials in construction, but the road approaches on either side, being parallel and close to the stream, the bridge wings adjoined the main stem essentially at right angles, with a rounded effect to form an "S" shape.

Another "classic in stone" was the old "Great Crossings" bridge on the Youghiogheny River at Somerfield, Pa., just a few miles northwest of the point where the National Road crossed from Maryland into Pennsylvania. When the Youghiogheny Flood Control Dam at Confluence was built about 1940, this old National Road bridge, and in fact, the whole Village of Somerfield, disappeared under water. The bridge was and probably still is, in excellent state of preservation at the bottom of Youghiogheny Reservoir.

Other short turnpikes and connecting roads adjoined the main roads described above, but many of the latter were unpaved and difficult to travel—particularly in wet weather.

The beginning of the Canal era in Pennsylvania, about 1835, was a serious blow to the old privately operated turnpikes of Pennsylvania, as much of their passenger and freight traffic was diverted to the canals. The rapid rise of railroad transportation in Pennsylvania in 1850 sounded the death-knell of the old turnpikes, and except for local roads feeding the railroads, the inter-city pikes deteriorated to the point where long-distance wagon and carriage travel was virtually non-existent. It was not until the advent of the horseless carriage in the early 1900's that Pennsylvania's old turnpikes under State and Federal direction, were restored and began to share the transportation load of the State once again.

CANAL BRIDGES AND AQUEDUCTS

While there were canals in Pennsylvania as early as 1797, the canal boom in this State really started when the Pennsylvania Canal Commissioners broke ground for the Pennsylvania Main Line Canal, with much ceremony, at Harrisburg, July 4, 1826.

Within the next eight years the State had constructed canals along many of the major rivers of the State and had a combination of canals and State railroads linking Philadelphia with Pittsburgh along a fantastic 395 mile route known as the "Main Line."

Canal freight and passengers, and even whole sections of canal boats were transported overland from Philadelphia by rail to the canal basin at Columbia. From Columbia the boats proceeded by water to Hollidaysburg, at which point they were boosted 1400 feet over Allegheny Mountain on the Allegheny Portage Inclined Plane Railroad, and travelled by water again from Johnstown to Pittsburgh.

Privately owned canals sprang up in areas not serviced by the State canals. By 1840 there were some 1250 miles of canals either in operation or under construction in Pennsylvania.

Bridges on the canal routes were of three types. First were the short foot bridges at the lower end of each lock to permit the lock tender to operate his miter-type water gates from both sides of the lock. As the lock side walls were seldom more than 17 feet apart, a short plank-type bridge several feet wide, with a railing, served the purpose, and also provided a pedestrian crossing.

An interesting suspension bridge used by mules to tow Lehigh Canal boats across the Lehigh River east of Bethlehem, Pa. Built 1857. (Courtesy Hugh Moore, Jr.)

Jackstown Aqueduct, a cast-iron, wrought-iron truss structure which carried the Juniata Division Canal across a creek near Mt. Union, Pa.

A second type of bridge was required wherever an existing road was cut by the canal. As is the case with our modern limited access highways, it became the responsibility of the canal builders to provide adequate canal crossings for these roads without interferring with the flow of traffic on either transportation medium. Since the canal channel seldom exceeded 50 feet in width, a single-span bridge of about 60 to 70 feet in length sufficed, and was generally built wide enough for one-way wagon traffic. These bridges were usually covered, to preserve them, and the supporting structure was frequently the Burr-arch, or other truss arrangement popular at the time.

Aqueduct near Amity Hall carrying the Main Line Canal across the Juniata River.

Interior of the Juniata aqueduct showing Burr arch construction and water channel.

The Aqueduct

A more interesting problem was presented by the third type of bridge on the canals—the aqueduct. Because of the necessity for close control of the level of water in the canal channels there were only certain points at which external water was admitted, and then only through control gates or locks opening to a reservoir, or a dammed section of an adjacent river. Consequently, when the canal route crossed a creek or river which was not used as a "feeder," the canal right-of-way, like a highway, was simply carried over the stream on a water bridge or "aqueduct."

The construction of these aqueducts gave the bridge builders of the 1820's and 30's real headaches because of the tremendous weight of the water channel carried as a constant—not an intermittent—load. There was argument about designing for the additional weight of loaded canal boats using the aqueduct, but with normal water displacement the only additional load while a boat was in transit, was the weight of the mules on the towpath.

Nevertheless, design weights much greater than those for a normal highway bridge of the day had to be taken into account. There was also the problem of rotting out of the wood timbers, which frequently supported the water channel. For this reason masonry canal aqueducts were more desirable and required less maintenance than the wooden variety. Generally there were more wooden aqueducts built in the early canal days than masonry, particularly at sizable creek or river crossings.

Masonry aqueduct on the Main Line Canal at Newport, Pa., in wintertime. (Courtesy Mr. & Mrs. Alfred Wolpert.)

41

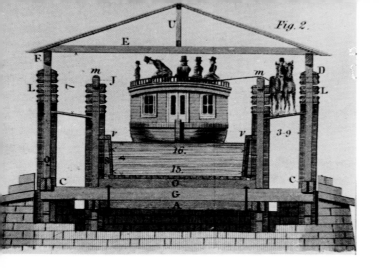

Patent drawing of the Allegheny River Aqueduct bringing the "Main Line" into downtown Pittsburgh. (Courtesy Dr. Ernest H. Coleman)

One of the most interesting early wooden canal aqueducts was the 1092-foot long wooden structure which carried the Main Line Canal across the Allegheny River into downtown Pittsburgh. This aqueduct was built in 1829 by a Mr. Lothrop of Pittsburgh, at a cost of $104,000. It had six piers and seven Burr-type arches of 150 feet span each. The overall width of the aqueduct, including pedestrian walk on one side and mule towpath on the other, was about 34 feet, with a water-channel (or "trunk") 16 feet wide at the top, 15 feet wide at the bottom, and 5 feet deep. Depth of water carried was generally about 4 feet, 3 inches. The arches (four to a span) were reinforced with a Long-type wooden truss, although most of the floor weight was supported directly on vertical 1-1/2″ iron rods hanging from the arches.

The entire structure was surmounted by a peak-roof to protect the wooden arches from external weathering.

Difficulties were encountered with this aqueduct on several occasions. At one time a section of the channel bottom dropped out, draining water out of good portions of the canal system on both sides of the river. Flood damaged various individual spans. In 1845 a fire destroyed the aqueduct. It was rebuilt by John Roebling using a wire cable suspension structure, as previously described.

Covered bridge at Clarks Ferry showing the towpath to pull canal boats across slack water in the Susquehanna River at its junction with the Juniata. (Courtesy James A. O'Boyle, Brooklyn, N.Y.)

42

Abandoned aqueduct and tunnel (circa 1875) on the Western Division of the Pennsylvania "Main Line" near Tunnelton, Pa., saving canal mileage along the Conemaugh River. (Courtesy of Richard Steinmetz.)

Other "Main Line" Canal aqueducts of importance were the wooden Juniata Division aqueduct crossing the Juniata River near Amity Hall, the stone aqueducts at Newport and Tunnelton, as well as aqueducts at Freeport and Middletown.

On the Delaware and Hudson Canal, in the northeastern part of the State, were several more Roebling aqueducts, as previously described. There was also a sizeable aqueduct on the Susquehanna Division Canal near Selinsgrove.

The advent of the railroads in Pennsylvania, which began in earnest about 1845, spelled the beginning of the end for the canal era. Some of the more financially successful enterprizes, such as the Lehigh Canal and the Monongahela Navigation, continued operation into the twentieth century, but most of the canals in Pennsylvania were shut down by 1903. The canal road crossing bridges were dismantled almost immediately. The lock keepers bridges survived for a time at least while the lock masonry remained intact.

The abandoned wooden aqueducts soon fell to pieces of their own weight, but many of their sturdy piers may still be seen in the streams and rivers throughout the State.

An aqueduct on the Delaware Division canal at Point Pleasant, Pa., showing surplus water discharging to the Tohicon Creek below. (Courtesy Dr. Ernest H. Coleman)

Gustavus Wilhelm Samuel Nagle is credited with the construction of the Northern Central Railroad Bridge across the Susquehanna River between Marysville and Dauphin in 1858, approximately 4000 feet long. Wrought-iron trusses are shown replacing some of the original wooden arches, washed out by floods.

EARLY RAILROAD BRIDGES

Railroads in Pennsylvania were being built as early as 1827. In that year one of the first railroads in the United States was built at Mauch Chunk, as part of Josiah White's "gravity railroad," used in bringing coal down from Summit Hill to the Lehigh Canal. In 1834, the Pennsylvania Canal Commissioners opened the Allegheny Portage Railroad, as well as the State-owned Philadelphia and Columbia Railroad. Motive power on the very early railroads were horses or mules. By 1829, however, a practical steam lococotive had been developed in England, and within the next decade or two, steam-powered railroads began to supplant canals throughout the State.

Samuel H. Kneass constructed this second Market Street Bridge across the Schuylkill in Philadelphia to replace Timothy Palmer's "Permanent Bridge" in 1850-53 without interruption to traffic. The new bridge carried the Philadelphia-Columbia Railroad into downtown Philadelphia. (Courtesy of George R. Wills.)

Wooden Bridges

Early railroad rolling stock was fairly light in weight, so the problem of conveying the new medium over streams was at first handled by the same type of wooden bridges which previously carried the old turnpike traffic. Major railroad bridges of wooden construction were built at Market Street, Philadelphia, for the "Main Line" into the downtown area, as well as the well-known "Columbia" bridge across the Schuylkill at the foot of the old Belmont Plane.

An existing wooden bridge (longest covered bridge in the world) across the Susquehanna, Columbia to Wrightsville, was adapted for an independent railroad line connecting Lancaster and York. The Cumberland Valley Railroad crossed the Susquehanna at Harrisburg on a wooden Town lattice-truss type bridge.

The Pennsylvania Railroad, chartered in 1846, built its first major bridge across the Susquehanna at Rockville, Pa., a combination of Burr arch and Howe truss wood construction. The Northern Central Railroad built a similar wooden bridge just north of the Pennsylvania Railroad crossing at Dauphin.

Wood bridges carried early railroad traffic satisfactorily, in spite of the ever-present danger of fire from locomotive sparks, until about 1845.

First iron-truss railroad bridge in the United States, built in 1845 by Richard Osborne for Philadelphia and Reading Railroad. It was located near Manayunk, Pa. Removed in 1902.

A timber trestle on the Stewartstown Railroad in York County, Pa. (Courtesy Oram Bell)

By this time railroad rolling stock was becoming more sophisticated, much heavier, and a need for a radical improvement in bridge design for railroad use was being felt.

Prior to this, bridge building had been primarily a matter of craftsmanship, wooden-model testing, and "trial and error"—mainly by skilled carpenter-designers.

However, a new breed of bridge designers were developing—Col. Ellet, John Roebling, Herman Haupt (of Gettysburg, Pa.) and Squire Whipple—who, for the first time, applied mathematical principles in computing stresses in bridges. Some basic guide-lines to the understanding of truss action were published, independently, by Whipple and Haupt in the 1840's and, happily, were in agreement.

Iron Railroad Bridges

There now developed a trend toward the use of iron in bridges—cast iron for compression members and wrought iron for bridge members in tension. The first such bridge was designed by Squire Whipple in 1841. The movement toward iron bridges gained momentum until 1850, when a metal truss bridge on the New York and Erie Railroad at Lackawaxen, Pa., collapsed while a train was crossing it. Following this fiasco, the New York and Erie ordered the removal of all its metal bridges and re-conversion to wooden structures. For a few years metal bridges were in disrepute.

Typical cast iron-wrought iron structure on the Pennsylvania Railroad Main Line near Malvern, Pa. On the track is a special photographic car and engine sent out in 1869 to photograph all major bridges, tunnels, and other structures between Philadelphia and Pittsburgh. This is one of the original photos, developed enroute in the "Photograph Car." (Thomas Norrell Collection)

Combination iron arch and truss bridge at Coatesville, Pa. on the Pennsylvania Railroad. (Collection of Thomas Norrell, circa 1869)

In spite of this the trend to metal railroad bridges picked up again, often using the Pratt and Howe truss types originally developed for wooden bridges. Vertical wooden members gave way to cast iron cylindrical or octangonal tubular pieces, with the diagonal members being converted to wrought iron "straps." Scientific calculations entered into the design, based on the compressive strength of cast iron and the much greater tensile strength of wrought iron.

Octagonal cast iron vertical members and wrought iron braces on the Pennsylvania Railroad bridge near Perryville, Pa. (1869 Pennsylvania Railroad Company Photo)

Octagonal post iron bridge east of Lancaster on the Pennsylvania "Main Line."

Such confidence developed in metal bridges that unusually high-span viaducts and tressle-type structures began to appear around the State. Typical of these was the Kinzua Viaduct over Kinzua Creek in Hamlin Township on the Bradford branch of the New York, Lake Erie and Western (now the Erie) Railroad in northwestern Pennsylvania.

This viaduct, at the time of its completion, in 1882, was the highest bridge in the world, towering 301 feet above Kinzua Creek. It carried a single-track on an 18-foot wide deck across a 2052 foot gulf, using 20 viaduct towers supporting Warren type trusses. Fifteen hundred tons of wrought iron were used in the construction. (See also page 29 and back cover.)

Conemaugh Viaduct on the Pennsylvania Railroad east of Johnstown. Until destroyed by the Johnstown Flood, this was one of the largest and most spectacular stone arch bridges in the country. (Courtesy Dr. Ernest H. Coleman)

Mainville bridge on the Catawissa Railroad. Locomotive shown is the "Black Diamond" of the Philadelphia and Reading Coal and Iron Company. (Collection of Thomas Norrell)

The ordinary metal bridges which began to appear at railroad stream crossings throughout the State, however, were supplied by such firms as Keystone Bridge Company of Pittsburgh; Phoenix Bridge Company of Phoenixville, Pa., and other bridge building firms in neighboring States. Competition in keeping costs low also reduced what factors of safety may have been in use, and such things as "allowance for wind velocity" were unheard of. Bridge construction continued, using relatively light-weight tubular and rod construction while the weight of the locomotives, passenger cars and freight cars increased.

It was almost inevitable that trouble was in the making. Starting in 1877, a series of railroad bridge failures swept the country, with considerable loss of life. Public faith in metal bridges sank to a new low.

The 1869 "Photograph Special" crosses an interesting metal arch and Howe truss bridge at Sherman's Creek near Duncannon, Pa., on the Pennsylvania Railroad.

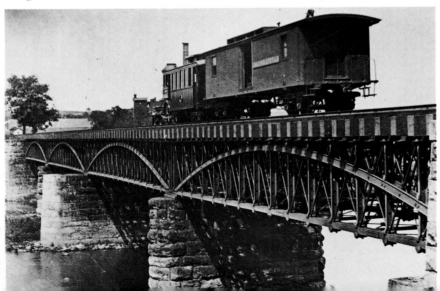

The "Stone Bridge" at Johnstown built by Pennsylvania Railroad in 1887 withstood the Johnstown Flood of 1889. (Courtesy Irving London)

Stone Arch Bridges

So alarmed was Pennsylvania Railroad by the failure of existing metal bridges that they began converting all their bridges to stone-arch construction—a much more expensive, but certainly a more enduring type than the available cast iron-wrought iron structures. Out of this development evolved such famous structures as the "Stone Bridge" in Johnstown (1887), so strongly built that it withstood the Johnstown flood several years later—as well as the present Rockville Bridge across the Susquehanna—built in 1902—the longest stone arch railroad bridge in the world. The Pennsylvania Railroad viaduct at Coatesville and the Delaware crossing opposite Trenton were also rebuilt in stone.

The "bridge which was never finished" is represented by these old South Penn Railroad bridge piers in the Susquehanna River at Harrisburg, looking east. New York Central abandoned this project, sometimes called "Vanderbilt's Folly,"* in 1885. (Photo by author.)

*See "Vanderbilts Folly," (1989 printing) by W.H. Shank.

This wooden trestle, built in 2½ days, temporarily replaced the Conemaugh Viaduct to bring the Pennsylvania Railroad back into service east of the stricken Johnstown area following the 1889 Flood. (Courtesy Irving London.)

There were some examples of stone arch railroad bridges in existence even before the metal bridge failures of the 1870's. One such "classic" is Starrucca Viaduct in northeastern Pennsylvania on the New York and Erie (now a part of the Erie) Railroad. This 110-foot high stone structure, built in 1847-48, originally carried a single track of the Erie over Starrucca Creek, at its junction with the Susquehanna River near Susquehanna, Pa. It has 17 flat arch spans, each 51-feet long, and the total length of the structure is 1200 feet. So well built was this viaduct that it is today still carrying Erie rail traffic, now two tracks wide, and live loads many times heavier than those which first passed over it in the 1800's.

Steel Bridges

The ultimate answer however was steel, a light yet strong metal with working strength 20% greater than wrought iron. Steel had previously been extremely expensive, but with the development of the Bessemer converter in 1856 and the open-hearth method of conversion in 1867, commercial structural steel became practical and economical.

With the trend to steel bridge construction there also developed the realization that special engineering talent was necessary. Thus a new breed of professionally trained bridge engineers rapidly came into being, who set standards, who insisted upon destructive testing machines for bridge materials in the interest of public safety, and held the line against· unsafe cost-cutting procedures.

The unusual Starrucca Viaduct of 1848 was the subject of many a 19th Century artist's handwork. Built by James Kirkwood. (Courtesy Gallo Studios, Cleveland, Ohio.)

After 138 years the Starrucca Viaduct still carries heavy traffic, like the Erie Limited shown here. (Courtesy Erie Railroad Company)

Engineering colleges quickly incorporated courses in their curricula for investigation of all factors involving structural design. Materials testing machines were installed by bridge builders such as Pencoyd Iron Works, Pencoyd, Pa.; Phoenix Bridge and Iron Works, Phoenixville, Pa.; and American Bridge Company at Ambridge, Pa.

Bridge design, primarily as a result of the railroad boom of the 1850-1900 period, thus moved quickly from the wood craftsmanship stage; through the mathematically designed tubular, cast iron-wrought iron stage; to the professionally and scientifically engineered bridge stage, at the opening of the Twentieth Century.

It was a painful period in bridge development, but one during which many useful lessons were learned and during which much excellent literature on proper bridge standards was written.

Another development in the closing years of the 19th Century, which had important overtones for the future of American bridge-building, was the development of reinforced concrete, with iron or steel rods enveloped in concrete, so arranged that the metal bears the tensile stresses while the concrete handles the compressive loading.

The stage was thus set for the highly-developed science of modern bridge design, as we know it today.

A fine example of an early 20th Century railroad bridge, built in 1908, is this 1780-foot-long, cantilever structure designed by A.R. Raymer for the Pittsburgh and Lake Erie Railroad, crossing the Ohio River at Beaver, Pa. (Courtesy of Dr. George Swetnam.)

20th CENTURY BRIDGES IN PENNSYLVANIA

The year 1900, both calendar-wise and development-wise, is the logical point to begin our discussion of modern bridge design. A most important invention in American transportation history had caught the public fancy at that time—the horseless carriage. However, even such inventors as Duryea and Ford could scarcely have envisioned the tremendous changes which the automobile was to create in the entire American way-of-life, and transportation history in particular.

While American railroads (and their step-children, the electric "trolley cars") continued to handle a large portion of our passenger and freight service, the trend to automotive and motor-truck transportation began at the turn of the century. The first sign of change in this connection was better paving of major city streets in metropolitan areas where automobiles were in use. Then came the reclamation and hard-surfacing of some of the long-neglected inter-city highways and "turnpikes" of the early 1800's. Next came the development of secondary, urban roads. Pennsylvania, under Governor Pinchot, led the movement "to get the farmers out of the mud" in the 1920's and 30's. A network of small macadam "Pinchot Roads" replaced the old rural dirt roads. Finally, began the period of the high-speed interstate highway system, now nearly completed. The first forerunner of these high-speed interstate roads in the United States was Pennsylvania's famous Turnpike, the first section

A typical highway vehicle of the early 1900's was this 1909 Stanley "Steamer", fastest car on the road. This "Steamer" was owned by John Hartley of York, Pa., who sits at the wheel . (Note the "blow-out patch" on the left front tire.)

of which was completed, from Carlisle to Irwin, in 1940. In 1951, the Pennsylvania Turnpike was extended to the Ohio and New Jersey state lines to join similar turnpikes being constructed in those states. Today, four-lane, high speed interstate routes, most of them completed, a few still in construction, criss-cross the state. A significant development in 1970 was the opening of the Keystone Shortway (Interstate 80) which, cuts 75 miles off the previous New York-Cleveland Turnpike route.

Thus, in 75 years, has developed a completely new facility for land transportation—the modern motor highway system. American bridge engineers faced this exciting period in our history, in 1900, armed with the useful experience of the railroad bridge building era just ended, and with new and improved materials at their disposal. Fabulous bridge designs, merely dreamed about by 19th century bridge builders, now became practical reality. The possibilities for long-span bridges over water-separated areas were limited only by the imagination of the designers.

There were still some lessons to be learned, about such things as aerodynamic balance, for instance, but in general the American bridges produced since 1900 have been soundly engineered and many of them are still in service.

In Pennsylvania, we are surrounded by countless examples of modern bridge building at its finest.

A classic example of early 20th Century concrete bridge construction was the Walnut Lane Bridge in Philadelphia connecting the residential suburbs of Roxboro and Germantown across Wissahickon Creek, at a height of 147 feet. When completed (circa 1905) this was the world's largest single-span concrete bridge—having a clear center arch of 233 feet. At the ends were a total of five semi-circular arches each 53 feet wide. Total length of the bridge—585 feet.

Walnut Lane Bridge over Wissahickon Creek in Philadelphia, world's largest single-span concrete bridge when built. George S. Webster was chief engineer of the project; H.H. Quimby was bridge engineer.

The Erie and Lackawanna Tunkhannock Viaduct, built in 1915 near Scranton, was classified as the "Ninth Wonder of the World" due to its tremendous size and 240-foot height. Declared a National Historic Civil Engineering Landmark by ASCE in 1975. (Photo by the author.)

The Meadow Street reinforced concrete arch bridge in Pittsburgh was, around 1900, one of the most artistic as well as the largest new bridge of its type in the district, with a center span of 209 feet, three symmetrical 21-foot arches on each side, and a 454 foot overall length.

In the Scranton area, the Tunkhannock Viaduct, located about ten miles north of Scranton, is considered the "Ninth Wonder of the World", taking second place only to the Starrucca Viaduct, the "Eighth Wonder", some twenty-five miles further north. This masterpiece, in reinforced concrete, towers 240 feet above the bed of Tunkhannock Creek, with ten huge 180-foot concrete arches, plus two 100-foot spans buried in the fill at each end, for a total length of 2375 feet. It was built for the Erie and Lackawanna Railroad Company of Cleveland, which still maintains it. 162,000 cubic yards of concrete were used in its construction. The eleven piers are set on bedrock, two of which penetrate 92 feet below normal ground level. Work was started May 1912 and on November 7, 1915 the bridge was opened to railroad traffic. At the time, the tremendous structure was publicized as "the highest concrete railroad bridge in the world."

The largest single-span suspension bridge in the world, at the time of its building, was Ralph Modjeski's Bridge connecting Philadelphia and Camden. Opened in 1926 with elaborate ceremonies attended by

The 1904 Market Street Bridge at Harrisburg -- a steel-girder, two-lane structure which replaced the old "Camelback". In 1927 this Eastern Section was floated around the Island on barges and combined with the Western Section to make a four-lane bridge there, while the Eastern Section was replaced by a handsome, four-lane, stone-faced arch bridge designed by Modjeski and Masters.

Governor Pinchot of Pennsylvania, Governor Moore of New Jersey and President Coolidge, the bridge had a center span of 1750 feet and measured 8291 feet from portal to portal. Total weight of the original was 763,491 tons. 25,100 miles of wire were used in spinning its two cables. Total cost of the bridge was over 37 million dollars and thirteen lives were lost in its construction. In 1956, it was re-named Benjamin Franklin Bridge to distinguish it from the new Walt Whitman Bridge in southern Philadelphia, whose formal opening was held in 1957.

Three rather unusual bridges were built during the years 1926 to 1928 across the Allegheny River at Pittsburgh--at Sixth, Seventh and

The nearly-identical Sixth, Seventh and Ninth Street Bridges at Pittsburgh are "eye-bar chain" construction. Built for the Allegheny County Commissioners; V.R. Covell, Chief Engineer; A.D. Nutter, Chief Design Engineer. (Photo by the author.)

This sporty "1908 Gentleman's Roadster" was built by the Pullman Motor Car Company of York, Pa., at the height of the road-building revival in Pennsylvania (See "History of the York-Pullman Auto, 1903-1917" by W. H. Shank.)

Ninth Streets respectively. All three bridges were the so-called "self-anchored chain type", all similar, differing only in span length and corresponding details. One of them, the Sixth Street Bridge, received the first annual artistic bridge award of the American Institute of Steel Construction. This bridge replaced the heavy-steel truss bridge designed by Theodore Cooper in 1891 which, in turn, replaced John Roebling's famous Sixth Street span of 1857.

Tacony - Palmyra Bridge, opened in 1929 across the Delaware. A tied-arch bridge by Modjeski and Masters.

"The new and the old". This Gannett Fleming designed section of Interstate 81 on the outskirts of Scranton, Pa., towers more than 100 feet above the Erie Lackawanna Railroad in the foreground and the old "Crane Viaduct," a local landmark of long-standing. The new I-81 bridge piers are of the single-shaft, "hammer-head" type. (Courtesy Gannett Fleming Corddry and Carpenter, Inc.)

In 1929 a large and architecturally interesting bridge, another of Ralph Modjeski's creations, was opened across the Delaware River between Tacony, Pa. and Palmyra, N. J. It featured a "through tied arch" for the 551 main span, a double bascule, and multiple continuous deck truss spans, for a total length of 3658 feet. (The tied-arch includes a tension member, or "tie," connecting the ends of the arch--where effective arch abutments are not available to take up the thrust.) As the designer also pointed out, the tied-arch "provides a central feature of architectural prominence."

Concrete Bridges Popular

While the trend toward structural steel and cable-suspension bridges continued to grow in the early 1900's there was still considerable interest on the part of bridge designers in the use of concrete, or reinforced concrete, for medium and even long-distance valley crossings. The first solid concrete bridge ever erected in America, circa 1895, was a small one, 34 feet wide, over Pennypacker Creek at Philadelphia, with two spans 25 feet each. As a sort of afterthought, wire mesh was imbedded in the concrete for extra security -- probably how the reinforced concrete idea got started.

58

Many bridge students have classified the great 1902 Rockville Bridge, where the main line of the Penn Central crosses the Susquehanna River above Harrisburg, as a stone arch structure. H. G. Tyrell, however, in his 1911 "History of Bridge Engineering" says of this bridge : "Piers and spandrels are faced with stone, but the centers and the arch rings are concrete".

One of the best-known reinforced concrete arch bridges in America, which is also said to hold the record for long-span concrete highway bridges in the United States, is the George Westinghouse Memorial Bridge of 1930 over Turtle Creek Valley on Route 30 just east of Pittsburgh. Its outstanding feature is its tremendous 460-foot center span, flanked by spans of diminishing width for a total crossing length of 1510 feet, 235 feet above the valley floor below. An interesting construction feature was the use of steel centering for all the arches. An overhead cable system was used in handling materials to erect falsework and wooden forms for the pouring of the massive piers. Some 73,350 cubic yards of concrete were used in its construction, plus 3,500,000 pounds of reinforcing steel.

The Westinghouse Bridge is classified as a two-ribbed, open spandrel type, and is considered a fine example of the artistic use of concrete in bridge construction (even though a steel bridge would have been lies expensive) to produce a beautiful and well-proportioned structure.

George Westinghouse Memorial Bridge on Route 30 near Wilkinsburg. This bridge is believed to be the highest concrete arch highway bridge in the United States. (Courtesy Carnegie Library of Pittsburgh.)

Unusual, open, steel-grid deck bridge built at Laceyville, Pa. on the Susquehanna North Branch to replace the structure destroyed by the Agnes Flood of 1972. Solid concrete section provided for pedestrians and bicycles. (Courtesy of Gannett Fleming Corddrey and Carpenter, Inc.)

Public confidence is the long-span cable suspension bridge was considerably shaken on November 7th, 1940 when the beautiful Tacoma Narrows Bridge (over Puget Sound near Seattle, Washington) collapsed in a high wind storm just five months after its formal dedication. From the outset the bridge had shown some roller-coaster tendencies and was nicknamed "Galloping Gertie" even before its spectacular demise. Fortunately the only life lost was that of a small dog, who refused to leave his master's car, which went down with the bridge while the owner crawled to safety.

Certain bridge engineers, even before the disaster, argued that the bridge was improperly designed for the high winds common in that area, and after 1940, bridge engineers everywhere took another hard look at their aerodynamics calculations and added extra safety factors.

A spectacular bridge was designed by Ralph Modjeski's successors in 1948 for the Schuylkill River crossing of Penrose Avenue in southwest Philadelphia. The structural center portion of the bridge is a truss-cantilever with a graceful arch 680 feet long and two 340-foot side spans, for a total length of 1260 feet. The approaches consist of a number of girder spans, with a 9707-foot total length of bridge and approaches. Water clearance at the center span is 135 feet.

But the largest bridge ever designed by Modjeski and Masters in Pennsylvania, or perhaps by any other firm in this state, was the Walt Whitman Bridge of 1957 connecting South Philadelphia with Gloucester, New Jersey. This monster cable-suspension bridge has a main span of 2000 feet and a total length, including highway approaches, of 6.2 miles. The towers are 378 feet high, and the vertical clearance under the center span is 150 feet. (Photo; inside back cover.)

mmer-head piers of the
rman Wood Bridge
ce it safely above the
ter of the Susquehanna
Route 372. Buchart
rn design. (Photo by
author.)

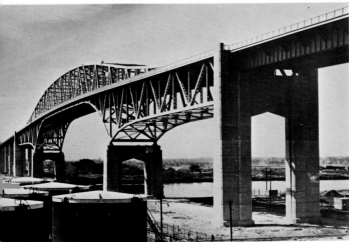

This unusual bridge
across the Schuylkill at
Penrose Avenue in
Philadelphia has a cen-
ter section which is a
combination of truss
and cantilever. (Cour-
tesy Modjeski and
Masters)

Construction view of the Jacks Run Bridge along the bank of the Ohio River, west of
Pittsburgh — 1931. Major feature of this bridge is its 420-foot reinforced concrete center
span, one of the longest in the country. (Courtesy of Robert S. Mayo, P.E., of Lancaster)

Pittsburgh has aptly been called the "City of Bridges". This aerial photo, made about 1969, shows most of the bridges "at the point" at that time, some already destined for demolition. On the Allegheny River (left) top to bottom are: the 16th Street Bridge; the Ft. Wayne R.R. Bridge; the 9th, 7th and 6th Street Bridges; the Fort Duquesne Bridge; and the Manchester Bridge (now gone). On the Monongahela River (top to bottom): a Railroad Bridge; the Brady Street Bridge (now replaced); the South 10th Street Bridge; Liberty Bridge; Panhandle R.R. Bridge; the Smithfield Street Bridge; the Fort Pitt Bridge and the Point Bridge (now gone). (Photo, courtesy of Richardson, Gordon & Assoc.)

The 1960 Fort Duquesne Bridge. A 423-foot tied-arch center span with four lanes of traffic at two levels. (Courtesy Richardson, Gordon & Assoc.)

The 1957 Fort Pitt Bridge, with a tied-arch center span of 750 feet. Four lanes of traffic at two different levels, north and south. (Courtesy Richardson, Gordon and Associates)

Aerial view of the twin bridges at Brookville, Pa., where the Keystone Shortway crosses North Fork of Red Bank Creek. (Courtesy Buchart-Horn)

Keystone Shortway

The building of the Keystone Shortway (Interstate 80), which runs across northern Pennsylvania through some of the most beautiful plateau sections of the State, provided Pennsylvania bridge designers with new challenges in crossing the deep gorges cut by major streams along the route.

Looking east beneath the west-bound span of the twin bridges at Brookville, 150 feet from stream to roadbed.

State's highest highway bridge on the Keystone Shortway at Emlenton, a Buchart-Horn project. This deck-truss bridge rises to the lofty height of 271 feet above the river bed of the Allegheny River below. (Courtesy Buchart-Horn.)

Construction of the Keystone Shortway, from Sharon, on the Ohio line, to Stroudsburg, on the New Jersey line was underway for about ten years, with various sections being opened to local traffic as they were finished. The entire 312.9 miles of the Shortway were officially opened to traffic in the summer of 1970, shaving about 75 miles off the New York to Cleveland high-speed route, which formerly followed the Pennsylvania Turnpike.

The most outstanding bridge on the Shortway is the state's highest highway bridge, designed by Ted Andrzejewski of Buchart-Horn, a compatriot of Ralph Modjeski. It is located at Emlenton, where the Keystone crosses the Allegheny River gorge, and where three of the state counties come together. Buchart-Horn engineers, who also designed many miles of the Shortway right-of-way, elected to cross the deep gorge with a deck-truss type bridge (super-structure underneath the roadway) at a level of 271 feet above the river bed, making this bridge even higher than the celebrated Golden Gate Bridge at San Francisco -- and the fifth highest bridge in the United States. The Emlenton bridge is 1668 feet in length, 68 feet wide, and its large double-column concrete piers are located, two in Venango County, two in Clarion County, and the southwest abutment in Butler County. The cylinders for the major rivers piers are 19 feet in diameter, tapering to 16 and a half feet directly under the bridge super-structure. Brodhead Construction Company of Aliquippa was the contractor;. The bridge was opened to traffic in 1968.

Another unusual structure on the Shortway, also designed by Andrzejewski and Buchart-Horn bridge engineers, was the twin-bridge crossing of the North Fork of Red Bank Creek at Brookville. Two widely separated spans, one 1078 feet long and the other 1000 feet, of continuous plate girder construction provide such a pleasing addition to the countryside that Mrs. Lyndon B. Johnson presented Penn DOT with a special "Citation of Merit" for the artistry of design of the twin bridges and their esthetic value in preserving the natural beauty of the area. Several of the piers of the bridges were located directly in the reservoir for the Brookville water supply, and great care was exercised during construction to prevent any possible pollution of the area drinking water. The bridge was completed in 1963.

Other outstanding bridges on the Shortway are the Clarion River crossing, a bridge similar to that at Emlenton, designed by Modjeski and Masters; the twin Mifflinville Bridges in Columbia County which won the 1966 American Institute of Steel Construction Award for their designers - Brookhart and Tyo ; and the Twin Moshannon Viaduct Bridges joining Clearfield and Center Counties by Brookhart and Tyo -- 1969 AISC award winners.

Clarion River Bridge on the Keystone Shortway -- similar in design to the Emlenton Bridge, rising 195 above the Clarion River, with an over-all length of 1635 feet. (Courtesy Modjeski and Masters.)

Recent Major Bridges

A recently opened structure in downtown Pittsburgh is the Brady Street Bridge over the Monongahela, designed by Buchart-Horn. The north-side approaches to this bridge were complicated by the multi-level structures of the Boulevard of the Allies, under and over which the Brady Street ramps and main feeder had to pass. The 620' tied-arch center span has a deck width of 80 feet.

The old Brady Street Bridge was removed after the new bridge was opened, but not without complications. The demolition crew had arranged their charges to blow the bridge to pieces, but when the blast was set off only the end-charges were effective, and the entire bridge structure settled (intact) into the Monongahela River — effectively tying up heavy boat and barge traffic for the next several weeks!

In 1974, The Commodore John Barry Bridge across the Delaware River between Chester, Pa., and Bridgeport, N.J., was opened. An extremely large cantilever-truss span structure, the bridge has a center span of 1622 feet, said to be the longest such cantilever main span of welded construction in the United States. Ship channel clearance is 192 feet. Total cost of the bridge was more than $125 million. 50,000 tons of steel were required. The designer was E. Lionel Pavlo.

Further north, the Betsy Ross Bridge was opened to traffic between Northeast Philadelphia and Pennsauken, N.J., in 1976. It is a continuous Through-Truss Bridge of 8,485 feet length (abutment to abutment) with a main span of 729 feet. Its width, (90-feet curb-to-curb,) makes it one of the widest bridges in the world. It has a ship channel

The Commodore John Barry Bridge, with abutment to abutment length of 13,912 feet, is the second longest cantilever highway bridge in the world. Its 1622-foot center span clears the water by 188 feet at the highest point. (Courtesy Delaware River Port Authority.)

The 1976 Betsy Ross Bridge is an eight-lane through truss span, with one of the widest roadways of any bridge in the world. (Courtesy Delaware River Port Authority.)

clearance of 135 feet. Total cost: $105,000,000. The Designer was Michael Baker, Jr., Inc. Connections are planned from this bridge (via the proposed Pulaski Highway) to Roosevelt Boulevard in north Philadelphia and the New Jersey Turnpike, via proposed Route 9.

Returning to the western part of the State, the completion of I-79 was made possible by the opening of the Glenfield Bridge across the Ohio about 1976, at Neville Island. The main span is a tied arch of 750-foot length. There are six lanes of traffic, plus 10-foot berms each side. The designer was Richardson, Gordon and Associates

We feel it is appropriate to include these outstanding modern bridges in our historic coverage of Pennsylvania bridges. They illustrate how far we have come from the primitive bridges of 200 years ago. Also, these bridges, built in the past quarter-century, will soon be our "historic landmarks" of tomorrow!

The Glenfield Bridge, where I-79 crosses the Ohio River, at Neville Island is the newest major bridge in Western Pennsylvania. A tied-arch of 750-feet length forms the center span, with 68-foot water clearance. (Courtesy Richardson, Gordon and Associates.)

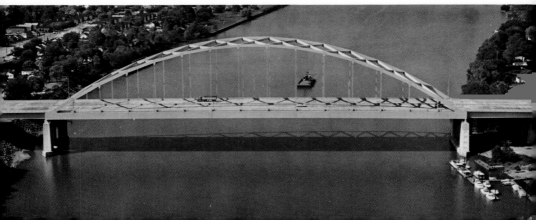

THE AUTHOR

"Historic Bridges of Pennsylvania" is one in a series of historical works authored and published by William H. Shank, professional engineer, historian and lecturer. The original edition of "Historic Bridges," published in December of 1966, was sponsored by Buchart-Horn, Consulting Engineers and Planners, of York, Pa. The current edition is published as a project of the American Canal and Transportation Center.

Mr. Shank's technical training includes a B.S. degree in mechanical engineering from Lehigh University, a tour of duty with the U.S. Army Corps of Engineers on the Manhattan Project at Oak Ridge, Tennessee, a number of years in the air conditioning and heavy mining machinery field and, more recently, several decades of experience in civil engineering promotional work.

In addition to "Historic Bridges of Pennsylvania", Mr. Shank has written "The Amazing Pennsylvania Canals," "Indian Trails to Superhighways," "Vanderbilt's Folly," "Great Floods of Pennsylvania," "History of the York-Pullman Automobile," "Three Hundred Years with the Pennsylvania Traveler" and "York, First Capital of the USA, 1777-1778".

ACKNOWLEDGEMENTS

The author gratefully acknowledges the considerable assistance of all of the following individuals in making possible the publication of this printing of "Historic Bridges of Pennsylvania" and its predecessors:

Richard Sanders Allen, Albany, N.Y.
Dr. Ernest H. Coleman, State College
Col. Robert E. Felsburg, Harrisburg
Capt. Thomas F. Hahn, Shepherdstown, W. Va
Herbert R. Hands, New York City
Gertrude E. Harley, Pottstown
Col. Russell E. Horn, York
Lt. Col. Wilbar M. Hoxie, Plaistow, N. H.
Benjamin F. G. Kline, Jr., Lancaster

Victor L. Lantz, Mt. Jewett
Wm. A. Lynch, Camden, N.J.
Robert S. Mayo, Lancaster
Hugh Moore, Jr., Easton
Edward H. Power, Pittsburgh
Christian L. Siebert, Jr., Camp Hill
Marcello H. Soto, Harrisburg
Dr. George Swetnam, Pittsburgh
George R. Wills, Lebanon

New Maynard Street Bridge at Williamsport, opened across the Susquehanna West Branch in 1987, looking south. (PennDOT photo.)

The new Sunbury Bridge (just above the "Fabridam") across the Susquehanna, was opened in 1986. (PennDOT photo.)

OTHER PUBLICATIONS OF THE AMERICAN CANAL AND TRANSPORTATION CENTER

THE AMAZING PENNSYLVANIA CANALS —170th Anniversary Edition— By William H. Shank, 10th Printing (2001). A much expanded variation of many previous printings. 125 illustrations, and tables of locks and mileages on most of the principal canals in the State, never previously gathered together in one volume. Four-color cover; two-color interior; 128 pages; a definitive work.

INDIAN TRAILS TO SUPERHIGHWAYS—By William H. Shank (2002 Printing). History of the development of Pennsylvania's historic roads and the many interesting vehicles used on them. Much Indian folklore and early colonial history. Descriptions of Braddock's Road, Forbes' Road, National Highway, Lancaster Turnpike, Plank Roads, Corduroy Roads, William Penn Highway, Lincoln Highway, Pennsylvania Turnpike and Keystone Shortway. Profusely Illustrated.

GREAT FLOODS OF PENNSYLVANIA — A TWO HUNDRED YEAR HISTORY— W. H. Shank, 8th Printing, (2001). Data, photos and non-technical text on all major floods in the Keystone State since records have been kept. The causes of floods and their alleviation and prevention are discussed. Full chapters on the Johnston Flood and the disatrous floods of 1936, 1955 and 1972 are included. A definitive work.

THREE HUNDRED YEARS WITH THE PENNSYLVANIA TRAVELER — By William H. Shank, 2nd Printing (2000). — Contains 156 pages of delightful text, written with humor and perception of the problems which beset Pennsylvania pioneers as they ventured westward from the Quaker City into Indian Territory. The text includes chapters on Indian trails, early roads and vehicles, river travel, pioneer bridge-builders, canals, aqueducts, inclined planes, gravity railroads, steam railroads, plank roads, bicycles, horse cars, cable cars, trolley cars, early automobiles, pioneer air vehicles - each chapter a complete book in itself. A virtual textbook of travel history in Pennsylvania. Heavily illustrated.

THE BEST FROM AMERICAN CANALS—Number 5 (1989-1991). A publication of the American Canal Society (1991) including a complete history of the Panama Canal, update on the Rhine-Main-Danube Canal, description of several Chinese canals, and navigation tips on the Black River, the Hennepin, the Alabama and the Florida waterways. 8 1/2 X 11 paperback with 88 pages.

THE BEST FROM AMERICAN CANALS—Number 6 (1991-1993). Genesee Valley Canal; Champlain Canal; D & R Canal Park; Lehigh Field trip; Mule-Power Analysis; British I.W.A. Visit; International Conference, Harper's Ferry; Mississippi River Field Trip; B & L Canal, Canadian Canals; Irish Canals; Biwa Canal-Japan.

THE BEST FROM AMERICAN CANALS—Number 7 (1993-1995). Shubenacadie Canal; Apalachicola - Chattahoochee - Flint Waterway; Canal du Midi - France; Hennepin Canal; Robert Fulton; D & H Canal; Ohio & Erie Canal; Green River; "The Shakers"; James Brindley; Erie Canal; Columbia & Snake River Navigation; International Conference - Augusta.

THE BEST FROM AMERICAN CANALS — Number 8 (1995-1998). Features a Panama Canal Tour and also covers outstanding articles published in the American Canal Quarterly. Journeys of the Canal Society of New York along the Erie Canal. The opening of the National Canal Museum in Easton, PA. The World Canals Conference in England. The "Venice of America." COMPLETE REPRINT OF Alvin Harlow's **When Horses Pulled Boats.**

THE CANALS OF NEW YORK STATE — 2nd Printing, (1995). Contains well-researched articles by American Canal Society members on the Empire State canals. New York was the training ground for early canal engineers. Scores of drawings, maps and photos bring the state's canals, old and new, alive in vivid detail.

THE COLUMBIA-PHILADELPHIA RAILROAD AND ITS SUCCESSOR—William Hasell Wilson, 1896. This book is an on-the-spot account of the building of one of the oldest railroads in America by its chief engineer, later resident engineer for the Pennsylvania Railroad, who purchased it from the Pennsylvania Canal Commissioners. This 1992 reprint is fully illustrated with 45 old photos, maps and drawings from the files of William H. Shank.

HISTORY OF THE YORK-PULLMAN AUTOMOBILE, 1903-1917—By William H. Shank, (1970). History of the "Six-Wheeler" Pullman, and its successors, which almost made York, PA the automotive capital of the United States. History of the early automotive industry in Eastern Pennsylvania also included. Profusely illustrated. An ideal gift for antique car buffs.

TOWPATHS TO TUGBOATS—A History of American Canal Engineering. By Shank, Mayo, Hahn and Hobbs (1995). The works of such famous Canal Engineers as Benjamin Wright, Canvass White, Charles Ellet, William Hamilton Merritt, George Washington Goethals are detailed —with the canals they built. The Erie, the Welland, the "Soo", the Panama, the St. Lawrence Seaway and the Tenn-Tom are among the many waterways described in detail. A 72 page, 8 1/2 X 11 book, the publication contains more than 130 drawings, maps and photographs in USA, Canada and overseas.

VANDERBILT'S FOLLY - A HISTORY OF THE PENNSYLVANIA TURNPIKE —W. H. Shank (Tenth Printing, 1993). The railroad war of 1880-85 which created the tunnels and roadbed for the present turnpike. History of the Turnpike, 1940-1985, included.

PICTURE-JOURNEY ALONG THE PENNSYLVANIA MAIN LINE CANAL, 1826 - 1857, By Philip J. Hoffman, P.E. (1993). Edited by William H. Shank, P.E. Full-color drawings of entire state-owned route, Philadelphia to Pittsburgh. 8 1/2 X 11 paperback. 80 pages. Full Hoffman biography included.

PENNSYLVANIA TRANSPORTATION HISTORY-A Supplement—By William H. Shank (1990). In this book, Mr. Shank has discussed media and devices not covered in his other books. Early river craft, rope ferries, steam boats, inclined planes, gravity railroads, early steam locomotives, horse cars, cable cars, trolley cars, elevated rail and subway systems, and air-travel devices are included. An 8 1/2 X 11 book with 72 pages and approximately 100 old photos, drawings and tables. Four-color cover.